Mishmeres HaKodesh V'HaChinuch
of the
Batei Din Tzedek of Kehillah Kedoshah Bnei Brak
POB 110, Bnei Brak • IVR 03-6768218 • Fax 03-5745504

בס"ד, אדר תשפ"ב

<u>Approbation</u>

We hereby approve the children's book
Seeing good, not bad, changes sad to glad!
written exclusively by Ahuva Raanan.

The contents have been reviewed
and found suitable for *yerei Shamayim*.
The author has merited *siyata diShemaya*,
publishing many children's books that promote values
important for raising Jewish children with good *middos*.

May we merit the blessing that
"we and our children know Your Torah."
אמן כן יהי רצון

Rabbi Mordechai Blau

Originally published in Hebrew as *Nireh et Hatov V'haetzev Ya'azov*

ISBN 978-1-68025-904-9

FELDHEIM PUBLISHERS
POB 34549
Jerusalem, Israel

208 Airport Executive Park
Nanuet, NY 10954

Illustrated by Sofi Agres
Translated by Aviva Rappaport
Proofread by Cindy Scarr
Graphic Design by Ettie Shmidov

www.feldheim.com

Ahuva Raanan

SEEING GOOD, NOT BAD, CHANGES SAD TO GLAD!

Translated by Aviva Rappaport
Illustrated by Sofi Agres

My Toolbox Books
For the development of emotion regulation in early childhood

It was morning, the start of a new day.

As soon as Rachel opened her eyes, she felt sad. She didn't even want to get out of bed.

At first, she didn't know why she felt like that, but then she remembered.

Today was Tuesday, the day her mother came home late. When Rachel got home from school, her grandmother would be waiting to greet her instead.

There was another reason Rachel didn't feel like getting out of bed.

It was because every Tuesday in school, they had an art class, and Rachel didn't like it.

With a sigh, Rachel got ready.

She left for school in a bad mood.

At recess, Rachel's friends went out to the schoolyard to play.

Rachel wanted to stay in the classroom. She wanted to talk to Avigayil, her best friend.

But Avigayil wanted to play outside. So Rachel stayed inside the classroom alone, feeling very sad and lonely.

Rachel took her lunch bag out of her backpack and found a note from her mother.

She read the note, but then thought bitterly, *How sad that Mommy's coming home late!*

She felt her throat get tight and tears spring to her eyes.

She returned the lunch bag to her backpack without even taking a bite out of her apple.

In the art class, she tried hard to draw a picture even though she didn't feel like it.

But the picture didn't come out good.

She tried again and again. Finally,
she crumpled up the paper
and threw it into the wastebasket.

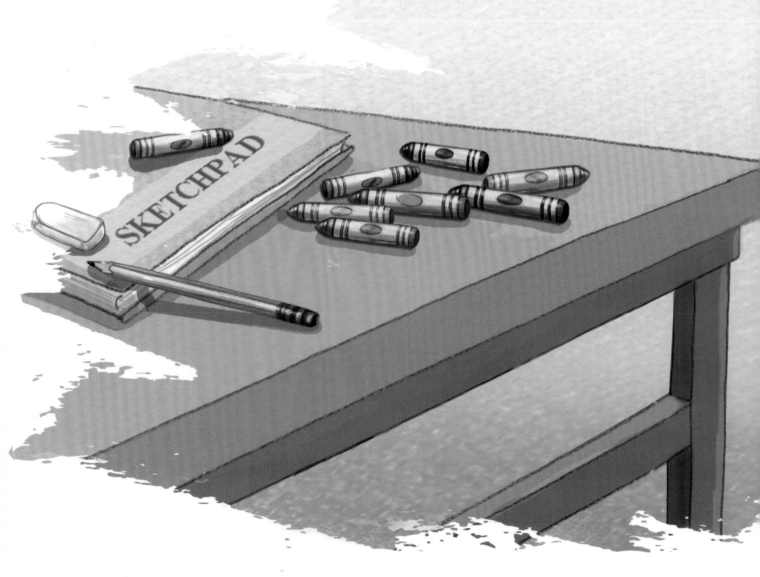

When school let out,
Rachel saw that the friends
she usually walked home with
had left without her.

The sadness inside her
got bigger and bigger.
Even though Miri started
walking next to her,
Rachel didn't feel
like talking.

When Rachel got home, her grandmother was there waiting for her.

Bubby greeted her with a big smile and a hug, but Rachel was still feeling sad. Bubby served a lunch of rice and some kind of patties Rachel didn't recognize. Rachel left most of it on her plate and stayed hungry and in a bad mood.

Then Bubby told her they were going to bake cookies together. Rachel thought, *What good are cookies when my best friends aren't really my friends and I can't even draw a nice picture?!*

After they finished baking cookies, Bubby suggested they look at Rachel's sticker collection.

That's a good idea! Rachel thought.

She started to feel happy and forgot a little bit about all the sad things in her day.

On the way to her room, she suddenly remembered that she had a new package of stickers she hadn't put in her album yet. Now would be a great time to do it! She took the album out of the drawer and excitedly looked for the new package of stickers.

But the package wasn't there!

Rachel looked through the pages of the sticker album again and again. Then she looked in her backpack and in the drawer. But no matter how hard she looked, she couldn't find the new stickers.

Bubby helped Rachel look, but no matter how hard they tried, they just couldn't find the new stickers.

"Maybe when Mommy comes home, she'll find them," Bubby said to cheer up Rachel. "Meanwhile, why don't you show me all your other stickers?"

Rachel sat next to her grandmother, feeling sad. She didn't feel like showing Bubby her sticker collection. What good was it without the new package of stickers?

**A whole week passed,
and then it was Tuesday again.
And that day...**

Rachel woke up with a smile on her face.
She got ready for school as quick
as could be. Her mother gave
her a big kiss, wished her a great
day, put a small note in her lunch
bag, and reminded her that Bubby
would be there to greet her when
she came home from school.

"Thanks, Mommy!" Rachel said,
giving her mother a big kiss.

I'm so happy Bubby is coming today!
Rachel thought.

*Maybe we'll make cookies or look
at my sticker albums or read books. It's
so much fun to have such a strong, smart
grandmother who's so full of energy come to
our house every Tuesday!*

During art class that day, the teacher told everyone to draw a playground with a slide, a swing, and a fence.

Rachel began drawing and tried hard to make a good picture. And when one of the lines came out crooked, she didn't let it bother her! She drew and drew and then colored it in until finally, she had an amazing picture.

Rachel felt smart and very pleased with herself.

At recess, Rachel had a lot of fun playing with her friends. But when school was over, once again they forgot to wait for her.

Rachel walked home with Miri instead. They talked and laughed together the whole way home. They had such a great time that Rachel suddenly felt she'd made a new friend.

Rachel was happy to see her grandmother when she got home. At the beginning of the meal, she took just a few small bites of the food. But after those few bites, she discovered that Bubby's food really was delicious, just like Mommy always said.

All of a sudden, Rachel felt confused. She didn't know what was going on!

"How can it be?" she asked Bubby. "Last Tuesday, I was sad, but today I'm so happy!"

"That's how it is," her wise grandmother said. "Sometimes we're in a good mood, and sometimes we're in a bad mood."

"But, Bubby," Rachel said, "the same things happened on both days, but today they don't seem sad to me. Today at the beginning of the art class, I also couldn't draw. And after school, my friends walked home without me again. But this time it didn't feel so terrible."

Bubby looked at Rachel kindly, and said,
"It all depends on which glasses
you decide to wear."

"Glasses?!" Rachel exclaimed. "I don't wear glasses!
I see fine without them."

"I'm talking about imaginary glasses," Bubby
explained. "Each of us has two pairs of glasses
inside our mind. One pair is black, with dark
lenses. The other is pink, with rose-colored
lenses. When we wear the black glasses,
everything looks difficult and annoying.
But when we wear the pink glasses with
their rose-colored lenses, everything
looks easy, beautiful, and simple."

"Do you know what?" Bubby said. "Today, instead of making cookies, let's make two pairs of glasses: black ones and rose-colored ones!"

That sounds like fun! Rachel thought happily. *What could be better than making something with Bubby?*

Rachel and her grandmother went to a toy store and bought sunglasses with black frames, clear glasses with pink frames, and rose-colored cellophane. When they got back home, they went right to work. Bubby showed Rachel how to pop out the lenses from the pink frames, cover them with rose-colored cellophane, and put them back in the pink frames.

"Now," announced Bubby, "the time has come to try them on!"

Rachel put on the black glasses and looked around. Suddenly everything looked dark and gloomy, and very sad. Even her wonderful Bubby looked a little bit angry. The sticker album looked plain and boring.

"Oh no!" Rachel said. "It's like a nightmare!"

"And now, watch how everything
will change instantly," Bubby said.
"Put on the pink glasses, and you'll see
an amazing thing."

Rachel put on the pink glasses. Suddenly Bubby's face looked happy again, and the sticker album was colorful and exciting. Once again, the house was filled with light. All the gray and the sadness disappeared.

"Remember the rule," Bubby said. **"Seeing good, not bad, changes sad to glad."**

"I don't believe it!" Rachel said. "How could everything change in one second?
And all just because of what your eyes see."

You can decide to wear black glasses, but then you'll think everything's sad: things are annoying, the people around you aren't nice, your clothes are ugly, classes are boring.

Or, you can wear the rose-colored glasses and instantly feel happier and think things around you are better: classes are fascinating, people around you are amazing, games are fun, and your clothes are the best....

Bubby and Rachel continued playing. When Rachel's mother returned home later in the afternoon, they told her about their new game: the glasses game, a game where you learn to see good, and change sad to glad.

MY TOOLBOX

A series of books for the development of emotion regulation in early childhood

For parents, words to the wise.
And for children, a happy surprise!

Ways to cope and to inspire hope

A series of books for the development of emotion regulation in early childhood

My Toolbox Books
For the development of emotion regulation in early childhood

Emotion regulation

Emotion regulation, also called emotional regulation or self-regulation, is the process by which we manage and control our emotions. The goal is a balance between two opposite ways of dealing with emotions: denying their existence or allowing them unbridled release.

With emotion regulation, we express feelings. We don't suppress or deny them. But neither do we allow them uncontrolled release.

Using emotion regulation, we learn how to control our emotions and the way we express them by first learning to identify the emotion and understand it.

The importance of emotion regulation

A child's ability to regulate his emotions has a major impact on his healthy psychological development. Successful emotion regulation leads to emotional health and balance.

An emotionally balanced child can adapt to new situations and form relationships more easily. He can more readily overcome stressful situations and deal with pain or difficult emotions. Emotion regulation skills affect communication, social skills, self-image—actually, all areas of personal and interpersonal behavior.

Children who have difficulty regulating their emotions are less available for learning tasks and may be less well-liked by their peers. In contrast, children who use cognitive methods to control their emotions and behavior do well in school, have good social skills, and are accepted and well-liked by their peers.

The role of parents in a child's development of emotion regulation

A child's ability to regulate his emotions develops through his interactions with the significant figures in his life. The determining factor is how his parents react to his distress signals, his behavior, and the way he expresses his feelings.

From infancy, a child learns to organize and regulate his responses to stimuli he perceives from within (such as hunger or discomfort), and from without (such as sights, sounds, touch, and movement) with the help of his parents. He draws comfort from contact with them when they pick him up, hold him, feed him, and rock him until he calms down.

As the child grows, the parents' ways of calming him expand to include other options. They may comfort him through hugging and kissing, encourage him with reassuring words, or offer him different ways of dealing with his negative feelings. Such interactions bring children to gradually internalize the role of relaxation, and they learn to calm themselves in different ways.

Parental modeling of emotion regulation also plays a significant role, as the child observes and absorbs the way his parents respond to their own emotional states.

Ways to promote emotion regulation in young children

Recognize when your child is struggling with an emotion

The first stage in helping your child develop the ability to regulate his emotions is to create a safe emotional space for him. It's a place where you see things from your child's point of view and accept his thoughts and feelings without judging or criticizing them.

Ignoring or dismissing a child's feelings won't make them go away; it just makes the child feel that no one understands him, that there's no way to cope with such feelings, and that it's best to hide such feelings from the people closest to him.

But when parents create a safe emotional space for their child's feelings and issues, they help him learn how to control his emotions and cope with challenges.

Help your child identify and name the feeling

Words play an important role in the development of emotion regulation. Without words, it's impossible to identify an emotion, and therefore it can't be regulated. For a child to be able to regulate his emotions, he must recognize them, distinguish one from another, and name them.

Guiding the child to become aware of what he is feeling begins with spontaneous statements by parents as they identify the child's emotion and reflect it back to him. For example: "You're so happy right now!" Or, "You're tired and don't have any patience."

The more parents use emotion words to share their feelings, the more they help their child understand his own feelings and know how to express them.

Suggest ways to express emotion

Parents can help their child learn to regulate his emotions by teaching him legitimate ways to express his feelings. The goal is to acknowledge the feeling while encouraging him to control it.

Distressful or negative emotions can be regulated using various strategies:

1. Strategies based on contact with others. For example: sharing, asking for help.
2. Action-based strategies. For example: running, drinking, jumping rope, taking deep breaths, muscle relaxation.
3. Strategies based on mastery of thought processes. For example: distraction, delaying the response, reframing, and reassuring internal speech.

The My Toolbox series helps develop emotion regulation in early childhood

The My Toolbox series is designed to help young children develop emotion regulation skills. Each book in the series spotlights a specific, commonly experienced emotion. Rich illustrations and language bring to life various incidents that trigger the emotion. Feelings are named and described, giving the child the vocabulary to help him express his own feelings.

Each book also offers targeted strategies to help regulate the emotion:

💜 Through **identification with the protagonist** and his challenges, the child learns to recognize, name, and regulate his feelings just like the hero of the story.

💜 The rhyme taught in each book guides the child to achieve regulation by **changing his thoughts** and controlling them.

💜 The tool offered in each book lets the child adapt for his own use an **action or physical technique** that will help him manage and regulate the emotion.

Regulating the emotion of feeling sad

"It's a big mitzvah to always be happy."

(*Likutei Moharan 2, Tinyana, Torah 24*)

"מצווה גדולה להיות בשמחה תמיד".

(ליקוטי מוהר"ן תניינא, תורה כ"ד)

Parenting to encourage happiness

Events we encounter in our lives don't necessarily dictate our feelings or how we will react.

The human brain has two groups of neural mediators: those that engender feelings of pleasure and happiness, and those that cause negative feelings and feelings of distress.

The neural mediators from the first group block and moderate the effect of the second group's substances, thus creating a sense of well-being and peace.

Even when the surrounding reality is bleak, a wonderful neurochemical reality can be created in the brain, which will allow a person to cope with a complex reality with a sense of confidence and optimism. But the opposite is also true: even when the surrounding reality is wonderful, one can create a miserable neurochemical reality in the brain.

The way to increase the activity of neural mediators that bring pleasure and joy and help deal with sadness, anger, and fear is to share together times of fun activities filled with laughter and learning.

Parenting that encourages warm bonding, open expression of love, playing and learning together, creativity, laughter, and playfulness, strengthens neurochemical mediators and positive emotions.

In contrast, stress, anger, high expectations, being judgmental, comparisons, insensitivity, lack of availability, and lack of understanding and reassurance increase the presence of the stress hormone in the blood and its messengers in the brain.

In other words, happiness itself is the way to feel happy.

Positive thinking

The way we think has a big impact on our mood and functioning. Research shows that a positive perception of the self, of the world, and of the future will engender feelings of satisfaction and happiness, and increase the ability to cope with challenges and illness. In contrast, negative thinking is closely associated with depression, anxiety, and anger.

Fortunately, you can change your way of thinking and train your brain to think positively. The beginning is actually an awareness of what you're thinking. Next is to practice looking at things positively.

When parents model an understanding and compassionate approach to events (judging favorably), they help their child adopt an optimistic perspective of the world and develop good mental health.

A short exercise to change one's mood

To help ourselves or our child control our/his mood and change it to one that brings better results,
we can use the following techniques:

1. Identify:

We can help our child name his mood and accept it with understanding.

"You seem upset. Is something bothering you?"

2. Decide:

We need to bring the child to the realization that it's worth it to him to get out of this mood that's not serving him well. Best is to reach the point of an outright declaration to get into a different mood.

"It's hard to be in such a bad mood. Would you like to try to change it?"

3. Change:

Since thinking can be influenced through the body, we can, after deciding to change the mood and with the help of our bodies, enter another mood, even if we don't feel that way. How? By changing our facial expression and posture to more positive ones for a minute or two, we can immediately feel the surprising change.

"Let's pretend we're relaxed. How does a relaxed child look?"

It's worth practicing the transition between moods in real time. To do this, you can use pictures of children in different moods. As the child gets used to transitioning from one mood to another, it will be easier for them to control themselves in real time when they get into an unwanted mood.